MANAGEMENT OF AGRICULTURAL RESEARCH
A training manual

Introductory module

Prepared by

V.N. Asopa

Indian Institute of Management

and

G. Beye

Research and Technology Development Service

Research, Extension and Training Division, FAO

FOOD AND AGRICULTURE ORGANIZATION OF THE UNITED NATIONS

Rome, 1997

M-67
ISBN 92-5-104090-7

FOREWORD

There has been a tremendous development of agricultural research in developing countries over the past few decades, during which time investment in agricultural research from both national resources and international assistance has increased markedly. However, agricultural research institutions are generally managed by veteran agricultural research workers promoted for seniority rather than for management training and skills. Further, there are few courses available on the management of agricultural research, and solutions and models used in the developed world may not be appropriate for developing countries.

FAO has actively participated in strengthening the national agricultural research systems of developing countries, and has stressed the importance of effective organization and management for efficient research systems. The need for training in this area is great, and resources – particularly trained human resources – are limited. FAO has therefore developed a training programme on agricultural research management to support the training of trainers, with the expectation of a multiplier effect, and to facilitate a common perception of the structure and terminology of management, thus enhancing communication and understanding among agricultural research managers in discussing management problems, solutions and opportunities.

This training manual has been prepared as a basic reference resource for national trainers, to help them structure and conduct their own courses on management at the institute level. A separate manual will cover project and programme management. This manual is based on the four structural functions of management: planning, organizing, monitoring and controlling, and evaluating, each of which is covered in individual modules. Within each module, the manual addresses pervasive management functions, including motivating, leading, directing, priority setting, communicating and delegating, which are at all times a concern to all managers. Topics such as leadership, motivation, human resources management, policies and procedures are treated separately in individual sessions.

This manual as been designed for participatory learning through case studies, group exercises, presentations by the participants and participatory lectures. Throughout the manual, particular effort has been made to use the cases studied to capture the unique and rich experience of developing country research managers in tackling policy, programme and the day-to-day problems of managing research institutions and systems.

This publication is intended primarily for managers of agricultural research institutes in developing countries and for higher education institutions interested in launching in-service training courses on research management. However, it is hoped that agricultural research managers everywhere will also find it useful. The manual provides a course structure with contents that can be built upon and enriched. Users are therefore encouraged to send suggestions for its improvement.

Louise O. Fresco

Director

Research, Extension and Training Division

ACKNOWLEDGEMENTS

The task of preparing a training manual on Agricultural Research Institute Management began with the FAO Expert Consultation on Strategies for Research Management Training in Africa, held at the International Livestock Centre for Africa (ILCA), Addis Ababa, Ethiopia, 12-16 December 1983. Following the recommendations of the consultation, and on the basis of the curriculum design adopted, FAO embarked upon the preparation of this manual. In the process of its preparation, many agricultural research managers and management specialists have contributed. Besides the two main consultants, namely Dr Ronald P. Black, Denver Research Institute, University of Denver, USA, who prepared the first draft, and Dr V.N. Asopa, Professor at the Indian Institute of Management, Ahmedabad, India, who prepared the current version of the manual, the contribution of the following specialists in various fields must be singled out: Ramesh Bhat, J. Casas, A.K. Jain, F.S. Kanwar, V. Martinson, Gopal Naik, P. Nath, R.K. Patel, T.P. Rama Rao, S.K. Sharma, E.S. Tayengco, and J.S. Woolston. FAO expresses its gratitude to them all.

Special thanks are due to the International Service for National Agricultural Research (ISNAR), which has willingly made available its valuable experience and relevant materials throughout the preparation of the manual.

FAO also thanks all those authors and publishers who have allowed the use of copyright material from their publications, and the courtesy is recognized in each case.

This manual has been prepared under the responsibility of the Research Development Centre, Research and Technology Development Division, FAO, with the guidance of: Mohamed S. Zehni, former Director; and J.H. Monyo, E. Venezian and B. Müller-Haye, past Chiefs of the Research Development Centre. Scientific supervision was provided by G. Beye, Senior Officer, now Chief, Research Technology and Development Service.

TABLE OF CONTENTS

INTRODUCTORY MODULE

	Page
Introduction	1
Research management: a key ingredient	4
Components of a worldwide agricultural research management programme	5
Defining FAO's role	5
Modus operandi	5
The Manual	6
Evolution of the training manual	6
Coverage	8
Institute management	8
Pedagogy	9
User's guide	9
Design of the manual	9
Session sheet	10
Session guide	10
Instructional materials	10
Background readings	10
Recommended readings	10
Design flexibility	11
Workshop schedule	11
Organizing a training workshop	11
Appendix 1 – Management orientation and decision making	13
Understanding the situation	13
Will to act and action orientation	14
Problem-solving approach	14
Defining the problem	14
Generating alternatives	15
Specifying criteria	15
Evaluation and decision	16
Developing an action plan	16
Feedback and contingency planning	16

Appendix 2 – Case method   17

   What is a case?   17

   Types of cases   17

   Dimensions of a case   18

   Case discussion   18

   Usefulness of the case method   19

      Acquiring knowledge   19

      Developing skills   19

      Forming attitudes and values   19

      Behavioural learning   19

   Facilitating the process of learning   19

   Training of managers   20

Using the case method   20

   Sequential process of the case method   21

   Role of the resource person   22

   Role of participants   23

      Guidance to participants   23

   Utility of small group discussions   24

Case development and writing   25

   Identifying case development needs   25

   Developing case leads   25

   Initial clearance   26

   Data collection   26

   Preparing the case outline   26

   Preparing a case draft   27

   Clearance, registration and testing   27

Teaching notes   28

Appendix 3 – Summary of course contents   29

**Appendix 4 – Illustrative schedule for a workshop on agricultural research
   institute management**   31

Appendix 5 – Management training   37

Aims for management training   37

Some critical aspects of learning   37

   Motivation   38

   Participation and practice   38

   Feedback and reinforcement   38

Application of learning   38

Appendix 6 – Planning and management of short-duration, executive development programmes   39

Characteristics   39

Problems in managing SEDPs   40

     First-day problems   40

     Some participants switch off ...   40

     ... While others dominate   40

     All face mid-programme blues   40

     Total breakdown   41

     Non-academic concerns   41

     Suggestions to the programme coordinator   41

         Screening participants   41

         Planning the course and teaching material   42

         The first day   42

         On Subsequent Days   43

         Designing a learning climate   43

         Monitoring and reviewing the programme   44

     Suggestions to programme faculty   44

         First and last sessions   44

         Planning the programme   45

         Other aspects   45

     Suggestions to participants   45

References cited and sources for further reading   46

The other Modules are:

Module 1 – INSTITUTIONAL AGRICULTURAL RESEARCH: ORGANIZATION AND MANAGEMENT

Session 1. MANAGEMENT: THOUGHT AND PROCESS

Session 2. OBJECTIVES AND ORGANIZATION OF AGRICULTURAL RESEARCH

Session 3. ORGANIZATION OF INTERNATIONAL RESEARCH

Session 4. ORGANIZATION OF NATIONAL AGRICULTURAL RESEARCH SYSTEMS

Module 2 – RESEARCH PLANNING

Session 1. PRINCIPLES OF RESEARCH PLANNING

Session 2. THE INSTITUTE-LEVEL PLANNING PROCESS

Session 3. SETTING GOALS AND OBJECTIVES

Session 4. FROM OBJECTIVES TO AN OPERATIONAL PLAN

Session 5. PARTICIPATORY PLANNING EXERCISE

Session 6. CASE STUDY: PLANNING AGRICULTURAL RESEARCH IN MUGHAL SULTANATE

Module 3 – ORGANIZATIONAL PRINCIPLES AND DESIGN

Session 1. ORGANIZATIONAL THEORIES

Session 2. STRUCTURE OF AN ORGANIZATION

Session 3. ORGANIZATIONAL DESIGN AND CHANGE
Session 4. CASE STUDY: ESTABLISHMENT OF A DIRECTORATE OF RESEARCH AT
SORONNO UNIVERSITY OF AGRICULTURE
Session 5. CASE STUDY: ORGANIZATIONAL CHANGE AT SAMARU, NIGERIA

Module 4 – LEADERSHIP, MOTIVATION, TEAM BUILDING AND CONFLICT MANAGEMENT
Session 1. LEADERSHIP
Session 2. MOTIVATION
Session 3. TEAM BUILDING
Session 4. THE IRRI AGRICULTURAL EQUIPMENT PROGRAMME CASE STUDY: IRRI
MANAGEMENT COMPARES IRRI WITH DEVELOPING COUNTRY RESEARCH INSTITUTES
Session 5. CONFLICT MANAGEMENT
Session 6. CONFLICT MANAGEMENT CASE STUDY: DR AGADIR

Module 5 – MANAGING HUMAN RESOURCES
Session 1. RECRUITING AND MAINTAINING STAFF IN THE RESEARCH ENVIRONMENT
Session 2. THE PROFESSIONAL STAFF
Session 3. HUMAN RESOURCES MANAGEMENT EXERCISE
Session 4. PERFORMANCE APPRAISAL
Session 5. PERFORMANCE APPRAISAL CASE STUDY: SUZENE KOPEC
Session 6. EXERCISE IN DESIGNING PERFORMANCE EVALUATION FORMATS

Module 6 – MANAGEMENT INFORMATION SYSTEMS, COMPUTERS AND NETWORK TECHNIQUES
Session 1. MANAGEMENT INFORMATION SYSTEMS (MIS)
Session 2. MIS EXERCISE
Session 3. COMPUTERS AS MANAGEMENT TOOLS
Session 4. NETWORK TECHNIQUES
Session 5. PERT AND CPM EXERCISE

Module 7 – FINANCIAL MANAGEMENT
Session 1. FINANCIAL MANAGEMENT 1: COMPONENTS AND INFORMATION NEEDS
Session 2. FINANCIAL MANAGEMENT 2: PLANNING AND BUDGETING
Session 3. FINANCIAL MANAGEMENT 3: PROJECT DESIGN AND IMPLEMENTATION
Session 4. CASE STUDY: FARO ARROYA
Session 5. GENERATING FUNDS THROUGH CONSULTING AS AN INSTITUTIONAL
ACTIVITY. CASE STUDY: FOOD TECHNOLOGY RESEARCH INSTITUTE OF DONGAL

Module 8 – RESEARCH-EXTENSION LINKAGE
Single Session: RESEARCH-EXTENSION LINKAGE

Module 9 – INFORMATION SERVICES AND DOCUMENTATION
Session 1. SCIENTIFIC AND TECHNICAL INFORMATION IN A DEVELOPING-COUNTRY
RESEARCH INSTITUTION
Session 2: INFORMATION AS AN INPUT TO RESEARCH
Session 3: INFORMATION AS AN OUTPUT OF RESEARCH
Session 4: COOPERATION IN NATIONAL PROGRAMMES
Session 5: EXERCISE ON BARRIERS TO THE FLOW OF INFORMATION

Module 10 – INSTITUTE EVALUATION
Single Session: INSTITUTE EVALUATION

Abbreviations used in the text

CGIAR   Consultative Group on International Agricultural Research
ECA   UN Economic Commission for Africa
FAO   Food and Agriculture Organization of the United Nations
ICIPE   International Centre of Insect Physiology and Ecology
ILCA   International Livestock Research Centre for Africa
ISNAR   International Service for National Agricultural Research
MIS   management information systems
OAU/STRC/SAFGRAD Consultative Advisory Committee on Semi-Arid
          Food Grain research and Development of the Scientific Technical
          and Research Commission of the Organization of African Unity
NARS   national agricultural research systems
R&D   research and development
RDC   Research Development Centre
SEDP   short-duration, executive development programme
TAC   Technical Advisory Committee
TCDC   Technical Cooperation among Developing Countries

INTRODUCTORY MODULE

INTRODUCTION

In all of the fields of science, there is none that is more basic to the needs of humanity than agricultural research. Some have suggested that 'agricultural research is the oldest form of organized research in the world.' While this may or may not be so, individuals were making systematic attempts to apply scientific knowledge to improvement of agriculture by the middle of the eighteenth century. By the middle of the nineteenth century, organized agricultural research was taking place in institutions such the Agricultural Chemistry Association of Scotland, and the Agricultural Experiment Station, Möckern, Saxony. During the first half of the twentieth century, most industrialized nations developed extensive national systems for agricultural technology development, which received increased attention and resources following the Second World War. The practical benefits that accrue to society through systematic support of creation and use of scientific knowledge had been demonstrated convincingly to the world's leaders and to much of the general populace of industrialized societies. This belief that an investment in research would result in generous future returns was, and probably still is today, based largely on personal experience and observation. However, starting with Griliches' pioneering work in 1958, there has been a steady accumulation of economic analysis pointing to very beneficial returns from investments in agricultural research.

Prior to independence, agricultural research in many economies was largely focused on crops of economic significance for the colonial powers. The research institutions and experiment stations that emerged usually focused on plantation crops, and were staffed by expatriate scientists. Following independence, it was normal for governments to initiate research on improving agriculture to attain food self-sufficiency. This transition – from colonial to national agricultural research systems (NARS) – often started with fairly good research facilities and equipment, and some technicians. It was rare, however, to find a national who had been trained and nurtured to the level of a scientist, and rarer still to find such a person with managerial experience.

Still, at that time, the exhilaration of independence, the excitement associated with a new world organization that would maintain peace and focus resources on the betterment of mankind, and the awareness that science had and would further revolutionize the world, were all factors that made it hard to be pessimistic. It was in this environment that new NARS began to be formed and moulded in the developing countries, in parallel with similar scientific structures in other fields, such as industry and medicine. In industrialized nations, the scale of research operations had been changed completely by the end of the Second World War. Science had moved dramatically to the centre of the stage. Following the War, there was, to be sure, a change in focus, but not in the magnitude of the support. Science would lead to rapid development and agricultural research was riding the wave of optimism.

In developing economies, the most pressing problem was to produce adequate supplies of food. The world responded by creating the Food and Agriculture Organization of the United Nations (FAO), the first article of whose Constitution states:

"The Organization shall promote and, where appropriate, shall recommend national and international action with respect to:

(a)   scientific, technological, social and economic research relating to nutrition, food and agriculture;"

Developing economy governments rose to the challenge by setting up new institutions and expanding existing ones. In almost all countries, agricultural research was a favoured sector. The problems of hunger and malnutrition, it was expected, would fall to the march of science.

Forty years later there are still famines, and children go to bed hungry over much of the world. Malnutrition still saps the energy and mental vitality of a significant portion of the world's population.

The FAO 1992-97 Medium-term Plan notes:

"... by the end of the 1990s, there will be over one thousand million more people to feed than at the beginning of the decade. In addition, unless there are unprecedented shifts in income distribution, both from the North to the South and from the rich to poor within the South, the 500 to 1 000 million people who are currently underfed largely because they are too poor to buy sufficient food, will continue to go hungry."

What went wrong? Why did these new agricultural research organizations and resources not meet the expectations?

In retrospect, it can be said that the problems were much more complex than originally envisioned. Some would contend that scientific skills may have even been inadequate. Management skills obviously were not adequate, and hence a constraint.

During the eighteenth century, agricultural research was characterized by gifted individuals working on their own initiative, establishing and recording unrelated findings which had little impact on agriculture. A management innovation occurred in the nineteenth century, when learned farmers began to form societies with the objective of defining and solving their problems. Interacting with interested chemists, these societies took the initiative in setting up laboratories and field experiments. Agricultural science began to grow and develop in a systematic fashion, mirrored by improved farming methods and practices.

Looking back, the major questions addressed seemed to have concerned the nature and structure of the new organizations, the setting of priorities, the proper source of support, the relationship of research to the farmer, the relative emphasis to be placed on research and diffusion of research results, the degree of appropriate autonomy for the research organization, and other issues of management. It was only through effectively dealing with these management issues in industrialized economies that agricultural research was able to grow and lead agricultural development into the last quarter of the twentieth century. However, as noted earlier, agricultural research in developing economies moved into the same period with inadequate scientific skills and even fewer management skills.

The two very different situations in developing and developed nations both had a very similar procedural obstacle in the management of research organizations, namely:

> "The management of the research organization, at all its levels, is, in most cases, in the hands of veteran agricultural research workers who have risen from the ranks. This is as it should be. However, here we have people who, by training and inclination, have usually been conditioned to averseness to administration in all its manifestations. They are then made responsible for managerial activities in an extremely complex field, for which they have had little or no training whatsoever and for which their only qualifications are their individual character traits and standing with their research colleagues. Administrative understanding is usually incidental and rarely present."[1]

This occurs in both industrialized and developing economies, but with two significant differences.

First, in the hundred or so years that management has been a concern to agricultural research managers in the industrialized societies, a fair amount of management knowledge, expertise and capability has been generated and passed down from generation to generation. A new researcher, in say the United States of America, entering an agricultural research organization is surrounded by people who are fairly effective at managing at their level. The new scientist learns management on the job, the most effective way to learn most things. After independence, few developing-economy agricultural research organizations had indigenous management experience. Managers and staff have had to learn together.

The second difference has had to do with the general management environment. Toward the end of the nineteenth century, management became a discipline of importance in industrialized countries. In the early twentieth century, universities began to teach management, with a focus on industry. Today management is a serious concern of virtually all segments of society in industrialized countries. This is supported by a multi-million dollar annual business in management training in those countries. When one comes from a developing economy to an industrialized one, one is struck by the degree of organization, discipline, planning and management of virtually everything. This difference between the two types of economy works to the disadvantage of the developing-economy agricultural research manager.

RESEARCH MANAGEMENT: A KEY INGREDIENT

An FAO paper reviewing FAO's experience in strengthening NARS notes that FAO's first attempt to come to grips with research organization, planning and management issues at the national level was at an FAO European meeting held in London in October 1951. At the meeting, a survey of approaches to administration and financing of agricultural research by European countries was examined. It was also in 1951 that FAO appointed a part-time

---

1. Arnon, I. 1968. *Organization and Administration of Agricultural Research.* Amsterdam: Elsevier.

officer to deal with agricultural research. In 1962, the position was made full-time. A number of national projects with research organization and administration components were conducted. A research centre was established in FAO in 1972, which, in addition to national research support, also provided the Secretariat of the Technical Advisory Committee (TAC) of the Consultative Group on International Agricultural Research (CGIAR). These two functions were separated in 1976, and the Research Development Centre (RDC) became the focal point for research support activities in FAO, including sole responsibility for research organization and management aspects of FAO's assistance. In FAO's *The State of Food and Agriculture 1972*, it was noted that "... guidance in programming, administration, the establishment of appropriate institutions as models for new programmes, training in research techniques, and training of research directors, managers and administrators ..." were areas that deserved support.

From FAO review and planning missions and recommendations arising from expert consultations and seminars, increasingly the message was that poor management of existing human, financial and physical resources was the greatest bottleneck to agricultural research in developing economies. In late 1983, FAO convened an expert consultation on strategies for research management training in Africa, where one of the delegates, Dr Amir Muhammed, echoed the prevailing opinion: "Experience has shown that management capability becomes a limiting factor in getting the full benefits from an agricultural research system ..." Based on the recommendations of that consultation, FAO initiated preparation of agricultural research management manuals, and began a programme of regional and national management seminars and workshops. While concern was growing within FAO about management capabilities in NARS, this concern was reflected elsewhere.

It had become such an issue during the 1970s that the Rockefeller Foundation and the Government of the Federal Republic of Germany convened a meeting in Munich in April 1977 to discuss the possibility of creating and supporting a service to assist the development of NARS in developing economies. This meeting led to the establishment of a task force "to consider the need for an international service to strengthen national institutions and programmes for agricultural research." The task force concluded that "existing agencies ... cannot meet the pervasive needs of NARS in full." It was proposed that a new organization be established as a part of the CGIAR system to "concentrate largely on planning, organizational, and management issues." On 1 October 1980, the International Service for National Agricultural Research (ISNAR) was established. Its ultimate goal was "to enable developing countries to plan, organize, manage and execute research more effectively from their own human, natural and financial resources." Recognizing that this goal was more than any one organization could manage, ISNAR was instructed to "work in close cooperation with all international organizations, in particular FAO." ISNAR's constitution provided for a trial period of six years to test the need for the service. On the recommendations of an external review team, the ISNAR Board and TAC, ISNAR was subsequently made a permanent international institute in the CGIAR system.

COMPONENTS OF A WORLDWIDE AGRICULTURAL RESEARCH MANAGEMENT PROGRAMME

The primary components of a research management programme are training, consultancy, research, and communication. Training is important because it increases the skills of current managers, provides new information and enhances analytical skills. While there are a number of ways to accomplish this, in balancing costs and benefits one is drawn to a programme wherein a faculty trains a group of participants. This is the primary approach employed by FAO, ISNAR and other international agencies currently involved in management development activities.

DEFINING FAO'S ROLE

Training in management would help overcome management-related barriers to increasing agricultural productivity through effective agricultural research management. Some of the major constraints observed in developing economies are:

- inadequate management skills among both research and managerial staff of agricultural research institutions;

- a lack of institutionalized programmes to correct the situation; and

- a lack of awareness on the part of national agricultural research leaders of the urgent need for better management of research.

MODUS OPERANDI

The task of training is huge, while resources – particularly trained staff – are limited. Based on an extrapolation of data reported in an ISNAR external programme review, there were approximately 115 000 agricultural scientists in developing economies in 1990. All of these would benefit from an introduction to agricultural research project management, while about 10% would need the basics of research institution management. If one assumes 20 managers per course, it would mean 5 750 project management and 575 institute management courses. It is reasonable to assume that 5% of the scientists are new each year. Thus, just to meet the needs of new entrants, 288 project management and 29 institution management programmes would need to be held annually, even if there were no growth in the number of agricultural research scientists. The ten-or-less agricultural research management courses provided annually throughout the world, aimed at developing-economy agricultural researchers, is insignificant in comparison.

Besides the basic programmes, courses on specialized areas of agricultural research management, such as planning, organization, management information systems (MIS), evaluation, client-institute relations, personnel management, etc., are also needed. Programme evaluation activities have been shown to enhance the benefits of training.

Clearly, FAO and all of the other agencies active currently in strengthening agricultural research management skills cannot train all of the world's agricultural research managers. Even training the new entrants to the field is a job far beyond the combined capabilities of the few agencies involved.

The only feasible option under the circumstances is to train the trainers, in the expectation that it will have a multiplier effect. That would also help adaption of training to regional and country-specific needs. FAO has therefore initiated such training activity through preparation of this reference training manual, designed to be used as a basic resource by national trainers when structuring and conducting their own courses.

THE MANUAL

In earlier times, scientists pursued their research on an individual basis. Funds were never a problem and researchers continued their lines of inquiry on an open-ended basis. These activities were often not structured as projects, *per se*, i.e., they were without starting and ending dates, a budget, or specified technical productivity goals within the given budget and time frame. It was more common for researchers to work alone or in a loosely structured group conducting research in related areas. As projects, i.e., well defined programmes, with clear objectives, and institutions with interlocking programmes, have emerged, management has become more and more important to science. Yet this importance has not been reflected by changes in academic curricula. It is a rare PhD agronomist who has had management training. FAO's agricultural research institution management training manual will provide the basis for overcoming what is a major constraint on agricultural research productivity.

There are four distinct levels of agricultural research management that suggest themselves immediately as the targets for training programmes, namely the project, the programme, the institute, and the national. This manual focuses on the institute management level. National-level management is not given emphasis for several reasons, not least because FAO already consults with national-level managements on management problems within their NARS. Managers at the national level may not be as receptive to training programmes because of extreme demands on their time, and possibly a legitimate belief that they would not have reached where they are if they were not already good managers.

Managers at the institution level and below are more receptive to management training. Also, there is evidence that it is not long before managers from these lower levels, with their enhanced management capabilities, begin to move to national-level positions, taking with them their 'new' management skills and understanding. Therefore it is at lower management levels that FAO has focused this training manual.

EVOLUTION OF THE TRAINING MANUAL

The task of preparing a training manual on agricultural research institute management began with the FAO Expert Consultation on Strategies for Research Management Training in Africa, at the International Livestock Research Centre for Africa (ILCA) (Addis Ababa, Ethiopia, 12-16 December 1983). The expert consultation was convened to recapitulate research management training needs in developing countries, review some of the approaches being used and those planned to improve research management capabilities with particular reference to sub-Sahara Africa, and explore the possibilities and modes of cooperation among those institutions which are most active in this field. The scope for Technical Cooperation among Developing Countries (TCDC) and for North-South cooperation were also studied, and modalities for such cooperation were defined.

The consultation was attended by participants from Burundi, Cameroon, Ethiopia, Kenya, Pakistan, the Philippines, Nigeria, Senegal, Tanzania, Uganda and Zimbabwe. Representatives of the UN Economic Commission for Africa (ECA), Gerdat (France), the International Centre of Insect Physiology and Ecology (ICIPE), ILCA, ISNAR and the Consultative Advisory Committee on Semi-Arid Food Grain research and Development of the Scientific Technical and Research Commission of the Organization of African Unity (OAU/STRC/SAFGRAD) also attended as observers.

The expert consultation recognized the following:

* There was an urgent need for effective management of resources, as, in the foreseeable future, the situation was going to get worse owing to diminution of resources (land) and population increase.

* The status of agricultural research as a profession had to be enhanced by proper management capable of attracting funds and devising rewarding career structures.

* Training needs were identified at three major levels: national, institutional and project.

The expert consultation worked out a plan for training at the different levels (Table 1).

Table 1 Training needs of agricultural research managers

Subject area	Target group			
	Directors General	Directors of Institutes or Centres	Programme Leaders	Other staff
Programme Identification and Planning	U(A)	S	S	A for others
Financial Management	U	U(A)	U	S for Finance Officers; A for others
Personnel Management	U	S	S	U for Personnel Officers; A for others
Communication	U	U	U	U for Staff responsible for Public Relations
Documentation and Information	A	U	S	U for Research Officers; A for others
Operational Management	A	U	U	U for Transport and Auxiliary Services
Monitoring and Evaluation	U	U	U	S for NARS and Centre Economists
Extension and Linkages	A	U	U	U for Extension Specialists

Key: A = Awareness; U = Understanding; S = Skill.

Following the recommendations of the expert consultation, FAO embarked upon preparation of training manuals. Subsequently, two manuals were prepared by Dr R.P. Black, Denver Research Institute, University of Denver, USA. While one manual focused on institution management, the other focused on project management. These manuals were used in training programmes in Africa, Asia and elsewhere. A thorough review of these manuals revealed a need for re-design, concretization and capsulization. Copyright reading materials needed to be replaced by reading notes. Relevant case studies had to be developed, and incorporated into the modules. Following this review, work on preparing a training manual on agricultural research institute management began.

The manual presented here has been virtually rewritten, although the presentation style of the previous manual is retained. Reading materials based on available published literature have been incorporated to serve as required or background readings.

Coverage

Although this FAO manual does not currently focus on project management issues, they will be covered subsequently through a separate manual on project and programme management. The FAO approach aims to evolve a common perception of the structure and terminology of management. This will enhance communication and understanding among agricultural research managers in discussing management problems, solutions and opportunities. This FAO manual, while contributing to the establishment of a common perception of the subject, differs from other currently employed training approaches in an important way. The FAO approach provides a course structure with contents that can be built upon and improved over time. The current state-of-the-art should always be embodied in the FAO manual and associated training materials.

Other agricultural research management programmes are less standardized and are faculty-dependent. Some have course agendas that are fairly standard, but different faculty members may handle the same session differently, especially where consultants are normally used as faculty. There is nothing published to provide a basis for transferring session training capability to others or to provide a product for improvement. Many agricultural research management courses seem to be even more *ad hoc*. There is nothing wrong with this approach, and some training objectives may best be served by specially designed and implemented programmes. It is only that these programmes do not lend themselves as approaches for transfer and for continual growth and improvement in the way the FAO approach does.

Institute Management

While a better understanding of management concepts and of philosophical approaches, as well as many attitudinal changes, are needed, courses focusing on and emphasizing these are considered theoretical by many agricultural research scientists. Therefore, the FAO approach is to focus on management skill development – e.g., how to prepare an institution plan – and, in the process of presenting skills-oriented materials, to include information, materials, exercises and presentation approaches that will also achieve participant growth in conceptual, philosophical and attitudinal areas.

Institute management is built around the four structural management functions: planning, organizing, monitoring and controlling, and evaluating. These areas are covered in the manual, and are assembled in separate modules as this is the natural sequence in which they are a concern to a manager. First, a manager must plan. With a plan in hand, an optimal organization can be designed to carry out the plan. As the plan is implemented, the manager must monitor and control the activities in accordance with the plan. Finally, the institute activities are evaluated against the objectives and other standards set forth in the plan. A reading note (Appendix 1 to this module) introduces the frameworks for management orientation and for decision making.

Pervasive management-function activities, such as motivating, leading, directing, prioritizing, communicating and delegating, which are of interest to managers at all times, are treated while covering the structural functions. Also, in some cases, such as for leadership and motivation, individual sessions are programmed. Several specialized areas of management, such as human resources management and policies and procedures, are treated in their own set of sessions.

It must be recognized that the manual does not cover many issues which are specific to individual research institutions. It is expected that these issues will be raised and discussed at appropriate places during the training workshop.

Pedagogy

The manual has been designed for a very participative form of teaching, including use of the case method, group exercises, presentation by participants, and participatory lectures. Because of their participative nature, it might be more appropriate to call them workshops.

The case method is the main pedagogic tool used in the manual, admittedly even though all topics do not have cases. The resource persons should acquaint themselves with the case methodology to be able to effectively handle a case. A note on the case method is given in Appendix 2 of this module.

User's Guide

The manual is designed so that anyone with a knowledge of and experience with the session subject matter should be able to prepare and manage the session based on the session materials. In practice, those with past teaching experience are usually more effective teachers in the workshop context.

DESIGN OF THE MANUAL

The workshop training manual is presented in 11 parts, comprising this introductory module and ten teaching modules, namely:

Introductory module
Module 1   Institutional agricultural research: organization and management
Module 2   Research planning
Module 3   Organizational principles and design
Module 4   Leadership, motivation, team building and conflict management
Module 5   Managing human resources
Module 6   Management information systems, computers and network techniques
Module 7   Financial management
Module 8   Research-extension linkage
Module 9   Information services and documentation
Module 10   Institute evaluation

Each module is divided into several sessions of varying duration, depending upon the material to be covered. Each session is presented together with information on components supporting the trainer and the training function. Details of the modules and their associated sessions are summarized in Appendix 3 of this module.

Session sheet

The session sheet provides basic information concerning the session title, date, time, trainer (to be filled in for each FAO workshop), format, objectives, instructional materials provided, background readings provided and bibliographic references to recommended readings which are not provided in the manual.

Session guide

The session guide gives the trainer notes and comments which refer to instructional materials (exhibits, hand-outs, etc.). The guide provides a suggested approach to covering the subject. Exhibits illustrate in a sequential manner how a session can be handled. Every trainer, however, will have different experiences with respect to the subject and should therefore approach the topic from his or her own perspective, using the session guide as a background and reference source.

The session guides are suggestive in their approach. They are designed to draw upon the experience of the teacher using them. This flexibility allows them to design the programme around specific national concerns, or to be more general, as would be appropriate for regional and broader international audiences.

Instructional materials

Instructional materials are either exhibits – to be shown on an overhead projector, flip chart, or by some other means – or hand-outs to be passed on to participants at some specific point in the sessions. These materials and their use are described specifically in the session guide. In many cases, these exhibits are based on published literature.

Background readings

Background readings will be useful to the trainer in preparing for the session. They may also be distributed to workshop participants so that they can prepare in advance for the session. Background readings are included in the manual and are based on published literature.

Recommended readings

Recommended readings are further sources of information of potential use to the trainer, but are not themselves included in the manual.

Both background and recommended readings include extensive references which can be followed up by the resource person to help them handle the sessions more effectively.

Design flexibility

Each session with its set of materials – the session sheet, session guide, instructional materials and background reading – is designed to stand alone. This gives a workshop organizer great flexibility in designing a workshop. Programmes may be conducted using the manuals as they are, or, if so desired, modules could be selected from the manual for courses on more specific subjects. Additional material can be added and new cases included, each enriching the manual.

Workshop schedule

In scheduling sessions, the practice is to schedule various modules consecutively. However, in a short-duration programme, rapid switching from one disciplinary area to another reduces learning effectiveness. An alternative course is to schedule various modules in a sequential manner and cover them one by one during the period of the programme. An illustrative workshop design using this approach is presented in Appendix 4 to this module.

A full workshop day would normally comprise four sessions, with breaks for lunch and tea or coffee as appropriate. In some cases, shorter-duration periods may be necessary, which may increase the total number of sessions in a day. It is important to provide reading time in the evening so that participants can prepare well for the next day's sessions.

ORGANIZING A TRAINING WORKSHOP

The first step in planning a training workshop is to assess training requirements. This issue is discussed in Appendix 5 of this module. Since training workshops of the type discussed here are usually of short duration, it is necessary to properly plan and manage them. Some of the important issues involved in this are discussed in Appendix 6 to this module.

Introductory Module

Appendix 1:
Management orientation
and decision making

MANAGEMENT ORIENTATION AND DECISION MAKING

A major role of managers and administrators is decision making in each of the specific situations faced by them. To perform this role effectively, the decision-makers should first understand the situation, and then frame the issues or problems requiring decision making. Next, they must have the will to seek programmes of actions which are effective and implementable in the given situation. Finally, for developing action programmes, they should use the problem solving approach. Any training of managers, therefore, should be directed at improving their abilities to perform these three tasks.

UNDERSTANDING THE SITUATION

Managers make decisions in real and not hypothetical situations. They often face new and complex situations, with little resemblance to past or present situations because of the everchanging environment and people around them. Moreover, the situations do not present themselves in neat clean shapes, but unfold slowly. Decision-makers, therefore, needs to improve their knowledge and skills in understanding new and complex situations, even though information may be inadequate and future outcome uncertain.

To understand emerging new situations, a manager needs to ask a series of questions:
    Who is facing the situation?
    Who are involved in the situation?
    Who or what individuals, systems, organizations, forces in the environment, etc. could
        possibly become involved?
    What is happening where and when in the situation?
    What could be of significance to interested parties?
    What could relate to input, to process and to output?
    How are the 'What?' factors happening – where and when?
    How could the situation progress in future?
    Are 'What?' and 'Who?' linked in the situation?
    Why the what/where/when/how factors?

Why are particular individuals, systems, organizations, forces, etc., acting the way they are?

These questions are universal in understanding any idea, process, physical object, abstract thought or a system. In the context of decision making, they help in defining problems, generating alternatives and specifying criteria for evaluating alternative options.

WILL TO ACT AND ACTION ORIENTATION

The will to act or the action orientation of the decision-maker is another important parameter. It has often been seen that some managers can do excellent analysis but are not quite able to take effective and implementable decisions. Action orientation helps in (i) weeding out impractical alternatives, (ii) better assessing alternatives in taking an appropriate decision, and (iii) implementing with requisite responsibility the decision taken.

Ability to act and action orientation implies:
- a *sense* of what is critical and what is possible in a given situation, rather than a futile, time consuming search for the best solution;
- a *willingness* to make firm decisions on the basis of imperfect and limited data, carry out the decision taken, accept personal responsibility for the solution, and take the consequences of the decision;
- an *ability* to convert targets and objectives into accomplishments, and to create a vision for themselves, their colleagues (through whom the decisions would be implemented) and the organization and others concerned, for better implementation; and
- an *appreciation or realization* that most problems do not disappear even if tackled well – they recur in some other form, according to the decision taken this time.

PROBLEM-SOLVING APPROACH

A problem essentially means an area of decision making.

After understanding the situation thoroughly and realizing the need for action, a manager may find the problem solving approach useful to devise action programmes. The problem solving approach involves problem definition and identification of decision area, generating decision making alternatives, and specifying criteria for selection, assessing alternatives and the optimal selection, and developing an action plan for implementation, including a contingency plan.

DEFINING THE PROBLEM

Problem definition is one of the most crucial steps in the problem solving approach. A wrong definition of the problem would not only fail to resolve the issues involved but could also lead to more complicated problems. The following steps have been found to be useful in defining problems:

Step 1   List all concerns (symptoms), particularly from the point of view of the decision-maker in the situation (i.e., the answer to 'Who?' and 'What?' of the situational analysis).

Step 2	Diagnose (from the answers to 'How?' and 'Why?') the concerns in order to establish real causes.
Step 3	Establish decision (problem) areas, and prioritize them in order of importance.
Step 4	Evaluate – if appropriate decisions are taken in these areas – whether the overall situation would improve particularly from the decision-maker's point of view.

A knowledge of the problems encountered in similar organizations would be helpful in this exercise. Besides this, holistic as well as logical thinking would significantly help in understanding the nature of problems, their categorization into long or short term, and in prioritization.

GENERATING ALTERNATIVES

Having identified the problem, the decision-maker needs to generate appropriate alternatives for resolving the problem. An understanding of organizational and external constraints as well as organizational resources helps in identifying the range of feasible action alternatives open to the decision-maker. A proper assessment of what is possible helps them to rule out infeasible options. Sometimes the alternatives for resolving different problems are obvious. However, more often than not, there could be a real possibility of generating comprehensive alternatives, which could address more than one problem area while respecting differing points of view. The next step, after generating alternatives, would be to rank them, before actually evaluating them. The decision-maker should check whether the alternatives generated cover the entire range (collectively and exhaustively) available, and whether each is distinct from the other (mutually exclusive).

The skills which could help in discovering alternatives would be holistic and logical thinking to comprehend the situation, as well as creative skills in generating the options which fit the situation. Knowledge of both the internal and external environments of the organization and the subject matter pertinent to the problem (human relations, how scientists can be motivated, etc.) would also help in arriving at better alternatives.

SPECIFYING CRITERIA

The ultimate purpose of developing and specifying criteria is to evaluate alternatives and select the best one for resolving the problem. Criteria are developed from a proper understanding of the situation and the inherent goals, objectives and purposes of the organization and the decision-maker involved in the situation. They would also be influenced by the goals, objectives and purposes of other individuals, departments and organizations connected with the situation. Criteria could be economic, social or personal. For effective use, criteria should be specific and measurable through quantification or other means. They should also be prioritized to assist proper selection among alternatives.

The skills needed for improving the ability to specify criteria are basically two:
- *holistic skills*, for identifying broader aims, goals, objectives and purposes in a situation, and
- *logical reasoning*, for deducing the specific criteria and their prioritization from such higher-order considerations.

EVALUATION AND DECISION

Alternatives need to be evaluated against the specified criteria in order to resolve the problem. Also, the outcome of choosing any alternative is not known with certainty. Usually, any one alternative would not be uniformly superior by all criteria. As such, prioritization of criteria could help in identifying the best alternative. The decision-maker might explicitly consider trade-offs between alternatives in order to select the best. Assessments of alternatives among the criteria need to be made, given partial and limited information about the possible outcomes of the alternatives. A final check may yet be needed to see whether adoption of the best assessed option is:

- consistent with the requirements of the situation, bearing in mind the uncertainty involved,
- implementable, and
- convincing to others involved.

The skills needed for improving this phase would thus be the ability to analyse logically, the ability to infer implications based on incomplete information and uncertainty, and the skill to convince others about the decision taken so as to obtain approval or help in proper implementation, or both.

DEVELOPING AN ACTION PLAN

Once the alternatives are developed, an action plan has to be developed. This is essentially the implementation phase. In this phase, the decision-maker needs to decide who would do what, where, when, how, etc. The process of arriving at these decisions is just like the steps involved in the problem solving approach, except that the chosen alternative becomes an input to this step. This phase would require coordination skills to properly organize a variety of resources (human, material and fiscal) and develop a time-phased programme for implementation.

FEEDBACK AND CONTINGENCY PLANNING

For a variety of reasons, the original decision (chosen alternative) may not work well and the decision-maker may have to be ready with a contingency plan. This implies devising feedback mechanisms allowing monitoring of the status of the situation, including results of the action plan. It also implies anticipating the most likely points of failure and devising appropriate contingency plans to handle the possible failures.

The additional skills required in this step would be those of devising control and feedback mechanisms.

Introductory Module

Appendix 2:
The Case Method

CASE METHOD

The case method has long been accepted as an important method for training managers and administrators. It is a method of learning based on active participation and cooperative or democratic discussion of a situation faced by a group of managers. The method of discussion also replicates the manner in which most decisions are taken in practice. It also involves replicating discussions with supervisors, peers or subordinates. If properly used, it has the power to improve the acquisition of knowledge, skills and attitudes.

WHAT IS A CASE?

No universally accepted definition of 'case' exists. We may consider a case, to quote Carl Christensen, as

> "... a partial, historical, clinical study of a situation which has confronted a practising administrator or managerial group. Presented in a narrative form to encourage student involvement, it provides data – substantive and process – essential to an analysis of a specific situation, for the framing of alternative action programmes and for their implementation, recognizing the complexity and the ambiguity of the practical world."

Thus, broadly speaking, a case is a description of a situation faced by an individual or organization.

TYPES OF CASES

A case could be a one-page, or even smaller, description with very little quantitative or qualitative information, of a situation faced by a manager concerning just one of the aspects of management involving just another individual. This is usually termed a 'caselet.' It could also be extensive and detailed, forming what is called a 'comprehensive case.'

DIMENSIONS OF A CASE

Three possible dimensions encompass a large part of the case:

What is described. A case could merely describe an individual, an incident, an organization, or a system. On the other hand, it could describe a decision making situation faced by a manager, involving part or whole of the organization, with a focus on one or more of the elements of the problem solving approach.

Purpose. The purpose of a case may be either research or learning. If the purpose is learning, the emphasis could be on one or more of the forms of learning, namely acquiring knowledge, gaining skills, and developing attitudes and values.

Mode of description. The nature of presentation could be written, audiovisual or oral.

CASE DISCUSSION

The case method should more appropriately be called the 'case discussion method' as discussion in a group of co-learners is an integral part of the method. This involves the following steps:

- study of a case by an individual learner, analysis of the case, and development of a strategy and action plan from the point of view of the decision-maker in the case;

- discussion in a small group (6-10 individuals) of the individual learner's analysis and proposals, and consequent revisions, if needed;

- discussion in a plenary session (up to 80 to 100 individuals) with the help of a discussion leader (resource person/faculty member); and

- post-plenary session discussion with co-learners and discussion leader to consolidate the learning, if necessary.

Study and analysis of a case by an individual manager would bring to bear only that individual's knowledge, skill, experiences and attitudes in resolving the problems faced by the manager in the case situation. Discussion in small groups or a class by several managers, with their respective backgrounds, knowledge, skills and attitudes and values, has the potential to enlarge the perspective of each individual. Discussion is supposed to take place in a democratic spirit, where each participant is free to present their analysis and the rest of the class or group tries to assimilate and understand it. Co-learners try to see the similarities and differences in such presentations. On the basis of strong logic, and not brute force of lung power, the issues are analysed and final assessments made. Thus, through discussion in small groups and class, an individual would:

- acquire new knowledge, and learn about skills and attitudes possessed by others,
- reflect on the applicability of their own knowledge, skills and attitudes or values, and
- learn the art of listening to others, convincing others and social interaction in a group setting.

USEFULNESS OF THE CASE METHOD

The case method has been found to be extremely useful in acquiring knowledge, developing skills, forming attitudes and influencing behaviour.

Acquiring knowledge

In the managerial context, knowledge is, firstly, situation-specific concerning policies of those – both external and internal – who influence managers' actions, and, secondly, concepts, approaches and techniques expounded in the literature or by colleagues, or from other sources. A manager needs to acquire such knowledge, not merely as words but so as to be able to appropriately interpret it for improved decision making. In the case method, knowledge is acquired while grappling with a real-life situation and not in isolation of its context.

Developing skills

Development of skills involves an element of actually doing. The case method helps, through discussion of real-life situations, to discriminate properly between the situations where particular skills could or could not be applied. The practice part could be accomplished by doing the exercise repeatedly or using different cases over a period of time.

Forming attitudes and values

Formation of attitudes and values for adults is a time consuming process, as attitudes and values are fixed early in life. It seems that the discussion mode of the case method, particularly with co-learners, helps a great deal in re-examining the attitudes and values of managers. Such discussions in small groups should be characterized by a relaxed, tension free, non-evaluative atmosphere in which participants may discuss their own experiences. Exposure to different ways of looking at the same situation might provoke the process of re-examining one's own attitudes and values. Needless to say, the longer the duration of the programme, the higher the likelihood of more participants starting such personal re-examination and attaining a greater degree of change in attitudes and values.

Behavioural learning

Behaviourial learning is done mostly through on-the-job training and experience. However, the learning of attitudes and behaviour could be enhanced by supplementing the case method with the syndicate method and field project work. The syndicate method (discussions in small groups) is an integral part of the case method. Field projects are widely used in degree-type programmes to provide real life behaviourial exposure. It is, however, difficult to use this method in short-duration, executive development programmes (SEDPs).

FACILITATING THE PROCESS OF LEARNING

For any learner, the major motivating element in the case method is the process of grappling with a situation faced by another manager. A better identification with the situation leads to increased involvement and enhanced learning for the entire group of participants. Other motivating elements could be embedded in the process by which participants are selected by their organizations, possibly in combination with the interest they show in the programme. As noted earlier, an element of feedback also leads to improved learning of positively reinforced action. In SEDPs, depending on the maturity and experience of participants, the discussion leader or teacher may have to provide feedback to improve the learning climate. Participants would receive the feedback and develop their own mechanisms of improving learning. This would not only help in learning during a programme but also afterwards in real life.

The application of learning obtained through the case method is effective on two counts. Firstly, the learning instrument (a case) is just like the situation faced in real life. Secondly, the process of arriving at the situation in real life, i.e., discussion with peers, use of the problem solving approach, and convincing others about one's proposed action, also matches with the process used in the method.

TRAINING OF MANAGERS

The case method has been found to be quite successful for training managers and administrators in both conceptual and pragmatic considerations. Some of the important features and dimensions of the case method which have enhanced learning are:

- The approach suits the mission of training managers and administrators, which is not merely to know but to act, and, there too, not merely to act but to learn how to act. This matches with the everchanging and complex situations encountered by managers and administrators.

- The method provides practical experience in group behaviour, such as learning to listen, express and gain confidence in one's judgment.

- It helps individuals discover and develop their own unique frameworks for decision making.

- It is suitable for all three forms of learning: acquiring knowledge, gaining skills and developing attitudes and values.

- The resource person finds the method intellectually stimulating, as each group of participants raises different questions and group dynamics are always distinct, although the case being discussed may be same.

- It meets the learning and research needs of a resource person in a professional institution by requiring him or her to keep in touch with practice by way of writing cases and deep interaction with practitioners in the teaching-learning encounter.

- It is an economically efficient method for a class size as large as 60 to 100 participants. In comparison, on-the-job training and small group learning could be very costly and time consuming, besides having a narrower perspective.

USING THE CASE METHOD

The decision to use cases would be based on programme objectives, potential participant profile and contents of the programme. The case method of learning requires significant preparation by individual participants, discussion in a small group (of 6 to 8 members) before attending the class, class discussion by participants with the help and guidance of a resource person, and after-class discussion and reflection. The above processes take place each session, day after day, during the programme to achieve the programme objectives and to match the contents and the profile of participants. The learning from each class session and from the programme could be significantly influenced by some characteristics of short-duration executive development programmes.

SEQUENTIAL PROCESS OF THE CASE METHOD

The process of training through the case method involves the steps below.

(i) The case method involves preparation, both individual and in small groups, and also discussion with the help of a discussion leader (resource person) of a situation as described in the case. This is done with the aim of not only of solving the problems faced by the manager in that situation, but also of learning to solve problems by gaining repeated experience in resolving real-life problems through analysis and discussion of a variety of cases.

(ii) In stage (i) participants first go through and prepare each case individually by assuming the role of the decision-maker in the situation and then decide on appropriate decisions and action plans to resolve the problems faced. During this preparation, a participant struggles with, first, defining the appropriate decision areas; second, specifying objectives, purposes and criteria for resolving the issues; third, generating options to resolve the issues; fourth, evaluating the alternatives on the basis of information available, which is usually incomplete; and, finally, deciding the course of action and contingency plan on the basis of their best judgment. In other words, they apply a problem solving approach.

(iii) The individual participants next discuss their inferences and action plans in the forum of a small group of 6 to 10 participants. Different individuals might, and in fact do, come up with different inferences and action plans. Group members need to carefully listen, understand, and appreciate these different views, and thus expand their range of thinking as well as depth of analysis. For this to happen effectively, the group atmosphere should be as free as possible, and focusing on important issues.

(iv) In-class discussion is also like small-group discussion, except that the range of experiences encountered in the inferences and action plans may be much larger, and that there is also a discussion leader to help the class in its deliberations. To enhance class learning, individual participants can play different roles, involving presenting, listening, clarifying, synthesizing and generalizing. However, a participant or a group of participants should not try to dominate the discussion, and should try to convince rather than to impose their views on co-participants.

(v) After-class discussion should be used to reflect on class discussion. Synthesis should be made within the initial small group, aiming to arrive at both an improved understanding of, and better decisions made in, the particular situation, and also tentative generalizations about individual approaches, attitudes and values for improved decision making in the future.

(vi) The instructors assign the cases and associated readings for the classes, provide guidance, if any, for preparation, and make themselves available for any clarifications. They do a thorough analysis of the case and devise a class strategy for themselves, which includes:

- deciding the objectives of the session,

- how to open the discussion,

- whom to call on for opening the discussion, for particular clarification or synthesizing,

- decide on the nature of questioning to bring out certain crucial issues if participants do not touch those issues,

- how much direction to use in the particular case discussion, and

- how to close the discussion.

While doing all this, the resource person should not seem to teach but merely provide learning impetus and thought space during the course of class discussion.

(vii)   The programme coordinator, along with the programme faculty and support staff, creates a learning climate conducive to peer learning through planning as well as implementing both academic and non-academic components of the programme.

(viii)   The method as such demands time, effort, involvement and self-discipline from participants as well as from the programme teachers and resource persons. This could be frustrating, particularly at the beginning of a programme. However, as the programme progresses, the pace and quality of learning improve and is quite satisfying in terms of achieving the learning objectives.

ROLE OF THE RESOURCE PERSON

One of the critical components in the effective use of the case method is the degree of preparedness of the resource person. A poor case, poorly prepared by the participants, can still be a valuable learning experience if the resource person is fully prepared. The case method relies heavily on the leadership skills of the resource person.

The role of the resource person in a case discussion is basically to guide and direct. The objective is to keep the discussion moving towards useful goals, with a minimum of intervention. The resource persons should keep themselves in the background until they feel that direction has been lost, that there is a need for more analysis, or that the key points are not receiving proper emphasis. To be effective, the resource person:

- should be prepared;

- should be flexible. Accept the fact that this is necessary in using case materials. Try not to force the discussion along predetermined lines;

- should ask questions when necessary, but ask as few as possible to support the open nature of the decision without leading into unproductive channels;

- should never become emotionally involved in the case discussion; they should never advocate or oppose a particular idea; and

- should summarize at the end and leave time to pull together the key points of the case. Many participants will need assistance in drawing out concepts from the ongoing discussion.

Participants in the case method approach often feel uncomfortable because, more often than not, there is no single solution to the situation described in the case. There are likely to be no irrefutable principles of management highlighted by the case which can be remembered for use in future situations. There is no hard and fast answer. To resolve this dilemma, the resource person must make clear to the participants that the case method is designed to develop their analytical and judgmental skills. It is the process by which they reach their decision that is important. The objective of the case method is to nurture this thought process; not to communicate facts to be memorized.

ROLE OF PARTICIPANTS

The case method heavily relies on adequate preparation and analysis by participants. Discussions are best for cases which are short and can be analysed on the spot. Case materials should be given to the participants at least one day before the proposed discussion, together with both instructions as to the amount of time they should spend on case analysis, and some insights as to how the case should be analysed. The former is important since many participants underestimate the amount of effort needed for effective case analysis. For example, a 30-page case would require approximately one hour to read. A preliminary analysis might take a further hour, and a detailed analysis and preparation might take an additional one to three hours, depending upon the complexity of the case. Case analysis is clearly not something which can be dismissed in ten minutes just before the discussion.

Guidance to participants

The extent to which a resource person may wish to provide guidance as to the optimal line of analysis will depend on a number of factors, such as the complexity of the case, relative time available for its discussion, and the participants' experience and skills in analyses. If the case is complex and there is a strong possibility that the class discussion will fail to focus on the key topics, or if participants are inexperienced in handling cases – as they normally will be in research and development (R&D) management workshops – analyses and instructions are both appropriate and desirable.

The following is a general set of instructions, which could be given to workshop participants to help them with case analyses.

(i)   Read the case through quickly to get a first impression of what it is about or what the basic issues may be. Then, re-read more slowly and begin to note down the facts and quasi-facts supplied and their relationship.

(ii)   Once the data in the case have been itemized, analyse and determine the major as well as the secondary issues. The analysis itself can be done in several ways. For example, it may be conducted by

–   examining the background environment in which the organization operates and the events and circumstances leading to the points at issue, and

–   determining the major areas with which the problem is concerned.

Some major points for analysis, commonly encountered in analyzing R&D management cases are:

*   The nature of competitive R&D organizations.

*   The organization's reputation and how this affects the issues.

*   National economic conditions and their effect on the demand for R&D.

*   The characteristics of the user community for the R&D organization's services in terms of location and relationship to the R&D organization.

*   The characteristics of the organization's product, i.e., research, development, information, consultancy, etc.

- The nature of the extension activities that connect the laboratory to the ultimate user or benefactor of R&D results.

- The impact of end-user attitudes and interests on the R&D organization's outputs.

- The project initiation and approval processes in the organization and their implications.

- The willingness to delegate authority in the organization.

- The degree or urgency of the project.

- The amount of uncertainty involved in the project.

(iii)   As the analysis proceeds, several possible courses of action will become apparent. Each of these should be examined, retained, or rejected as the analysis proceeds.

Take note of both the strengths and weaknesses of each point. Few, if any, situations are totally correct or incorrect.

(iv)   The participant should try to realize when there is a need for more data and what information is needed, or, if they are not available, what assumptions should be made.

(v) Once all this has been done, it should be feasible to arrive at one or more decisions. It should be remembered, of course, that possible solutions, or approaches to them, are many, and others may develop an entirely different solution or approach. Both may be equally correct if the participant has thought through the analysis clearly and logically.

UTILITY OF SMALL GROUP DISCUSSIONS

In an attempt to lighten the workload, participants can be divided into groups to analyse and prepare positions on a case. Such group discussions have proven to be highly valuable, provided each participant has made his or her own prior analysis, and they should be encouraged. Additional insights, ideas and perspectives are often brought out in such discussions. Participants who are reluctant to speak out in plenary sessions will usually open out in group discussions. Also, for most workshops, small group discussions allow participants to discuss the case among themselves in their own language before having to discuss in the official language of the plenary session. In using this technique, however, care should be taken to ensure that some participants do not use group discussions as a means of avoiding the effort associated with an analysis of their own. It should be made clear that, unlike the lecture approach, the case method assigns primary responsibility to the participant. In order to maximize the benefits, they must maximize their own efforts. The resource person should move from one group to another during case discussions so as to be aware of the emerging analysis.

CASE DEVELOPMENT AND WRITING

Case development and writing should be an ongoing process for any institution using the case method. Its importance arises from the fact that recent cases not only provide an element of interest among programme participants, but also bring to the class the latest situations being faced by decision-makers.

IDENTIFYING CASE DEVELOPMENT NEEDS

Case development and writing needs arise in two different ways. First, some of the existing cases in current courses may need replacement by new ones as the old ones are too old to generate much interest among participants, or they do not adequately depict the current decision making scenario in real life. Second, an opportunity may arise to write an additional case which would be useful.

The programme coordinator or resource person should review the objectives of the training programmes, modules or sessions in which new cases could be used, and then should specify the contents to be covered, the major issues to be tackled, the level of decision making (middle, senior or top), and the type and size of organization desired. Such specifications would provide a somewhat sharper focus when searching for leads on appropriate cases.

DEVELOPING CASE LEADS

A case writer, having defined the case writing requirements and prioritized them, has to look for real-life situations. Several ways are open in locating such situations.

Primary sources Colleagues, alumni, participants in current executive development programmes, contact persons in organizations where consulting may be in progress or may have been provided earlier, and visiting executives could all be sources of case leads.

Secondary sources Scanning relevant reports (including reports of government commissions, departments, etc.), particular industry and trade papers and journals, and other relevant publications – all these could generate possible case leads. These need to be followed up by correspondence or personal visits to ascertain the possibility of developing the leads into cases from the point of view of availability of required information as well as willingness of the organization to allow their use.

Pursuing possible case leads The case writer needs to prepare a list of contacts and associated files, with names and addresses of contact persons and organizations, and prioritize them on the basis of *a priori* assessment of converting these into actual case leads. Some might suitable for immediate application, others at a later date, and still others may require additional effort, such as inviting the relevant executives for an oral presentation. Systematic recording and follow-up procedures need to be established in pursuing possible case leads.

INITIAL CLEARANCE

Getting initial clearance, preferably from top executives of the organization, is necessary for efficient time utilization in case writing. If this step is not followed, the time spent on developing cases is wasted.

It may be helpful to brief the contact executive as well as the top executive about the purposes for which cases are used, with assurances both of confidentiality while working on it and of its non-use until the case draft is cleared by the organization. While there could be benefits to the organization through discussion of the situation, care must be exercised in making assurances which cannot be fulfilled. In any case, initial clearance for writing the case should be obtained fairly early.

DATA COLLECTION

The real work of case writing starts by planning and implementing the data collection phase through secondary sources, both published and in-company, and primary sources (interviews with executives and other knowledgeable persons). In the first phase of data collection, the case writer familiarizes him- or herself with the situation. This could include scanning of published materials for understanding the industry and the organization, records or personal knowledge of colleagues about previous attempts at case writing on the organization, and other knowledgeable persons about the industry, the company and the phenomenon under study.

The second phase would begin with preliminary interviews with key decision-makers in the organization in order to understand the situation and acquire an understanding of what went into decision making. Following this, detailed data from both primary and secondary sources will have to be collected according to a work schedule.

While secondary data from outside the organization could be collected independently, many in-company documents are obtained whilst or as a result of interviewing executives. It may be useful to plan out the nature of data that the case writer is seeking since many documents may not be allowed to leave the organization's premises and so will have to be studied in the limited time available during the visit. This phase is like conducting research based on secondary sources of data as well as in-depth interviews of executives. It demands all the capabilities of a good researcher.

PREPARING THE CASE OUTLINE

The case writer may have prepared a preliminary case outline even before embarking on data collection, but, having collected the data, a firm outline of the case should be elaborated. Some of the elements to be dealt with in this phase are listed below.

- Identify the major issues in the situation and those which need to be highlighted in the case.

- A background of the organization, its situation and executives should be included in the case as it is relevant and useful in providing a perspective for the case analyst. Usually this description follows the opening paragraphs on the major issues in the case.

- The nature of information from secondary and primary sources and their sequencing in the text.

- Essential aspects to be included in the text, versus explanatory and supportive information to be put in exhibits or appendixes.

- A sequencing of items to provide for easy reading and comprehension, unless the purpose of the case suggests otherwise.

PREPARING A CASE DRAFT

The efforts put into preparing the case outline should help in writing the case draft. Additional considerations and suggestions are given below.

(i) The case writer must keep the focus on the decision-maker, and be faithful and objective in describing the situation. Therefore personal comments, reactions, etc., of the case writer must be avoided. The language and terminology used by executives or generally used in the trade or profession must be retained. If such terminology is not likely to be understood by participants, explanations should be given in a glossary.

(ii) A case should be written using a structure which promotes an easy flow of thought for better understanding and comprehension by the participant. For the same reason, the language of the case should be understood by the participant. Details could be increased or reduced according to participant's anticipated knowledge and ability, interest and experience.

(iii) A catchy title and dramatic opening will attract reader attention immediately. The length should be kept as short as possible so that no unnecessary time has to spent on reading to attain comprehension. Generally, cases are written in the past tense. The case writer must maintain complete confidentiality.

(iv) The final draft should be written with as much care as a professional journal article.

CLEARANCE, REGISTRATION AND TESTING

Clearance of interview transcripts needs to be sought from executives before finalizing the case draft, more so if they are quoted. Having written the final draft, formal clearance must be requested from the organization. The organization may suggest disguising the name of the organization, names of executives, financial data, etc. Disguise helps participants in concentrating on and discussing the case *per se*, without possible introduction of extraneous information from other sources. However, disguise should not distort the situation to the extent where the purpose of the case is defeated. Having made such changes, formal clearance must be sought and obtained.

After obtaining formal clearance, the case needs to be tested. This could be in two stages. First, it could be discussed among other faculty members. This is particularly helpful when case writing activity is new, and many faculty members are willing to participate in such an activity not only to help a colleague but probably also to learn from each other's experiences. Alternatively, the case writer could request experienced faculty colleagues to comment on or personally discuss the draft.

The second, and more useful, test should be on the kinds of participants for whom the case is prepared. It would be useful if another colleague is involved in this process to learn about how the case was discussed, what issues emerged, how were they analysed, was some critical information missing, was some available information irrelevant, etc. Depending on the reactions, the case could be revised.

The case should be formally registered so that issues of copyright, use and distribution are in proper form.

TEACHING NOTES

Writing a teaching note is an extremely important activity in the case writing process. It helps in checking the adequacy of the case for the purposes it was written, in describing its use, in ensuring that proper analysis can be done, and in outlining strategy of its use. A teaching note should cover:

- programmes in which the case could be used;

- position of the case in the programme and module for which it is intended;

- learning objectives, major or minor, which could be achieved by using the case;

- major issues and their analysis, both qualitative and quantitative;
- background information and reading which would facilitate learning from and use of the case;
- preparation required by the resource person and the participants;
- possible assignments for facilitating preparation and learning;
- strategies to be used by the resource persons to get the best out of the case;
- past experience in using the case; and
- what happened in real life (if the organization featured in the study allows the information to be shared).

Introductory Module

Appendix 3:
Summary of course contents

SUMMARY OF COURSE CONTENTS

MODULE	TITLE	SESSIONS
	Introductory Module	
Module 1 (4 Sessions)	Institutional agricultural research: Organization and management	1 Management: Thought and Process 2 Objectives and organization of agricultural research 3 Organization of international research 4 Organization of national agricultural research systems (NARS)
Module 2 (6 Sessions)	Research planning	1 Principles of research planning 2 The institute planning process 3 Setting goals and objectives 4 From Objectives to an Operational Plan 5 Participatory planning exercise 6 Case study: Planning agricultural research in Mughal Sultanate
Module 3 (5 Sessions)	Organizational principles and design	1 Organizational theories 2 Structure of an organization 3 Organizational design and change 4 Case study: Establishment of a Directorate of Research at Soronno University of Agriculture 5 Case study: Organizational change at Samaru, Nigeria
Module 4 (6 Sessions)	Leadership, motivation, team building and conflict management	1 Leadership 2 Motivation 3 Team building 4 Case study: IRRI Agricultural Equipment Programme: IRRI Management compares IRRI with LDE research institutes 5 Conflict management 6 Conflict management case study: Dr Agadir

MODULE	TITLE	SESSIONS
Module 5 (6 Sessions)	Managing human resources	1 Recruiting and maintaining staff in the research environment 2 The professional staff 3 Human resources management exercise 4 Performance appraisal 5 Performance appraisal case study: Suzene Kopec 6 Exercise in designing performance evaluation formats
Module 6 (5 Sessions)	Management information systems, computers and network techniques	1 Management information systems 2 MIS exercise 3 The computer as a management tool 4 Critical Path Method 5 PERT and CPM Exercise
Module 7 (5 Sessions)	Financial management	1 Financial management 1: Components and information needs 2 Financial management 2: Planning and budgeting 3 Financial management 3: Project design and implementation 4 Case study: Faro Arroya 5 Generating funds through consulting as an institutional activity, + case study: Food Technology Research Institute of Dongal
Module 8 (1 Session)	Research-extension linkage	1 Research-extension linkage
Module 9 (5 Sessions)	Information services and documentation	1 Scientific and technical information in a developing-country research institution 2 Information as an input to research 3 Information as an output of research 4 Cooperation in national programmes 5 Exercise on barriers to the flow of information
Module 10	Institute evaluation	Single session: Institute evaluation

Introductory Module

Appendix 4:
Illustrative schedule for a workshop on agricultural research institute management

	MODULE	
Day 1 (4 Sessions)	0830 - 0900 0900 - 1000 1000 - 1030	Registration Inauguration Tea/Coffee
	Module 1	**Institutional agricultural research: Organization and management**

	1030 - 1130
	1130 - 1230
	1230 - 1315
	1315 - 1430
	1430 - 1600
	1600 - 1630
		1 Management: Thought and Process
		2 Objectives and organization of agricultural research
		3 Organization of international research
		   Lunch break
		4 Organization of NARS
		   Tea/Coffee

		Reading time for next day's sessions
Day 2 (7 Sessions)	**Module 2**	**Research Planning**
	0900 - 1000 1000 - 1100	1 Principles of research planning 2 The institute planning process
	1100 - 1130	Tea/Coffee
	1130 - 1215 1215 - 1315	3 Setting goals and objectives 4 From Objectives to an Operational Plan
	1315 - 1430	Lunch break
	1430 - 1500 1500 - 1600	5 Group discussions on participatory planning exercise 6 Plenary session on participatory planning exercise
	1600 - 1630	Tea/Coffee
	1630 - 1730	Group discussions on case: Planning agricultural research in Mughal Sultanate
		Reading time for next day's sessions

	MODULE		
Day 3 (3 Sessions)	0900 - 1100	1	Case discussion: Planning agricultural research in Mughal Sultanate
	1100 - 1130		Tea/Coffee
	Module 3		**Organizational principles and design**
	1120 - 1315	2	Organizational theories
	1315 - 1430		Lunch break
	1430 - 1600	3	Structure of an organization
	1600 - 1630		Tea/Coffee
			Reading time for next day's sessions
Day 4 (3 Sessions)	0900 - 1100	1	Organizational design and change
	1100 - 1130		Tea/Coffee
	1130 - 1315	2	Group discussions on the case study: Establishment of a Directorate of Research at Soronno University of Agriculture (SUA)
		or	Group discussions on the case study: Organizational change at Samaru, Nigeria
	1315 - 1430		Lunch break
	1430 - 1600	3	Plenary session for discussion on the case study selected for group discussions
	1600 - 1630		Tea/Coffee
			Reading time for next day's sessions
Day 5 (3 Sessions)	**Module 4**		**Leadership, motivation, team building and conflict management**
	0900 - 1100	1	Leadership
	1100 - 1130		Tea/Coffee
	1130 - 1315	2	Motivation
	1315 - 1430		Lunch break
	1430 - 1600	3	Team building
	1600 - 1630		Tea/Coffee
			Reading time for next day's sessions
Day 6 (6 Sessions)	0900 - 1000	1	Group discussions on case study: IRRI Agricultural Equipment Programme: IRRI Management compares IRRI with LDE research institutions
	1000 - 1100	2	Plenary session on the IRRI case study
	1100 - 1130		Tea/Coffee
	1130 - 1315	3	Conflict management
	1315 - 1430		Lunch break
			Reading time for next day's sessions

	MODULE		
Day 7 (6 Sessions)	0900 - 0945 0945 - 1100	1 2	Group discussions on case study: Dr Agadir Plenary session on case study: Dr Agadir
	1100 - 1130		Tea/Coffee
	Module 5		**Managing human resources**
	1130 - 1230	3	Recruiting and maintaining staff in the research environment
	1230 - 1315	4	The professional staff
	1315 - 1430		Lunch break
	1430 - 1530	5	Group discussions on human resources management exercise
	1530 - 1600		Tea/Coffee
	1600 - 1700	6	Plenary session on human resources management exercise
			Reading time for next day's sessions
Day 8 (5 Sessions)	0900 - 1015 1015 - 1100	1 2	Performance appraisal Group discussions on case study: Suzene Kopec
	1100 - 1130		Tea/Coffee
	1130 - 1315	3	Plenary session on the case study: Suzene Kopec
	1315 - 1430		Lunch break
	1430 - 1600	4	Group discussions on exercise on designing performance evaluation formats
	1600 - 1630		Tea/Coffee
	1630 - 1730	5	Plenary session on exercise on designing performance evaluation formats
			Reading time for next day's sessions
Day 9 (5 Sessions)	**Module 6**		**Management information systems, computers and network techniques**
	1000 - 1100	2	MIS exercise
	1100 - 1130		Tea/Coffee
	1130 - 1315	3	Plenary session on MIS exercise
	1315 - 1430		Lunch break
	1430 - 1530	4	The computer as a management tool
	1530 - 1600		Tea/Coffee
	1600 - 1730	5	Network techniques
			Reading time for next day's sessions

	MODULE		
Day 10 (5 Sessions)	0900 - 1000 1000 - 1100	1 2	CPM exercise group discussions Plenary session on CPM exercise
	1100 - 1130		Tea/Coffee
	Module 7		**Financial management in an agricultural research institution**
	1130 - 1315	3	Part 1: Components and information needs
	1315 - 1430		Lunch break
	1430 - 1600	4	Part 2: Planning and budgeting
	1600 - 1630		Tea/Coffee
	1630 - 1730	5	Part 3: Project design and implementation
			Reading time for next day's sessions
Day 11 (7 Sessions)	0900 - 1000	1 or 2	Group discussions on case study: Food Technology Research Institute of Dongal Case discussion on the case study: Faro Arroya
	1000 - 1100		Plenary session on case study: Food Technology Research Institute of Dongal *or* Faro Arroya
	1100 - 1130		Tea/Coffee
	Module 8		**Research-extension linkage**
	1130 - 1315	3	Research-extension linkage
	1315 - 1430		Lunch
	Module 9		**Information services and documentation**
	1430 - 1600	4 5	Scientific and technical information in a developing-country research institute Information as an input for research
	1600 - 1630		Tea/Coffee
	1630 - 1730	6 7	Information as an output of research Cooperation in national programmes
			Reading time for next day's sessions
Day 12 1 Session	**Module 10**		**Institute evaluation**
	0900 - 1100	1	Developing a framework for institution evaluation
	1100 - 1130		Tea/Coffee
	1130 - 1230 1230 - 1315		Feedback session Valedictory function

Introductory Module

Appendix 5:
Management training

AIMS FOR MANAGEMENT TRAINING

An analysis of the major requirements for training managers and administrators suggests that a training programme should aim at enhancing their capability to (i) understand specific situations, (ii) orientate action, and (iii) use effectively a problem solving approach which involves (a) defining problems, (b) generating options to resolve the problems, (c) specifying the criteria to select the best option, (d) assessing options on the specified criteria and choice of option, (e) developing an action plan, and (f) developing a contingency plan.

Enhancement of the above capabilities requires an improved knowledge base, covering the organization and its functioning, the environment in which it operates, a conceptual knowledge to explain actions of the organization and the people forming it, and the theory, techniques and approaches for resolving organizational problems. Besides such knowledge, decision-makers would also need a variety of skills to diagnose situations, apply theories, approaches and techniques, and both listen to others' opinions and convince colleagues about their own inferences and decisions. Finally, in the absence of complete information, appropriate values and attitudes would be most useful in taking decisions, devising implementable action plans, and obtaining support for implementing action plans.

Any training programme aims at improving a mix of the three elements of learning: knowledge, skills and attitudes. As the level of responsibilities increase, the importance of attitudinal development is enhanced and that of gaining skills and acquiring knowledge reduces. Ironically, it is also more difficult to impart and imbibe development of attitudes and values, compared to gaining skills, and gaining of skills as compared to mere acquisition of knowledge.

SOME CRITICAL ASPECTS OF LEARNING

Learning is a complicated process in general, and more so among managers at different levels and in different functions of organizations. Besides, each may have developed their own ways, which differ from those of others. Yet, some general principles relating to the learner and the learning process have been found to be helpful in improving adult learning. The level of motivation of the learner is likely to affect learning positively. Three elements of the learning process which help in improved learning are (i) participative or active learning, (ii) reinforcement and feedback, both positive and negative, and (iii) applicability of learning to the learners' situation.

MOTIVATION

Motivation is positively related to learning. There could be a variety of motivations for individual learners: some want to learn merely for the sake of learning, others learn to improve their status, still others to master improved techniques and skills to do a job better, and still others learn to safeguard their current position. Whatever the reason, motivation has been found to be positively related to the extent of learning. The trainer should understand the diversity in motivational bases to relate to the learners for better individual and group learning. It may also be useful to pay adequate attention to the learner's requirements of a nature other than academic, i.e., comfort, food, timing, feelings of acceptance from the group and the resource person, etc. This would allow true motivation to spur the participants towards the goal of learning.

PARTICIPATION AND PRACTICE

Experience suggests that an active and participative method of learning with some minimum repetition leads to improved learning of a variety of knowledge and skills.

FEEDBACK AND REINFORCEMENT

It is well known that positively reinforced learning leads to retention, whereas negatively reinforced learning leads to avoidance. In a training programme, such reinforcement could come from test results, feedback from colleagues (co-learners), feedback from resource persons, or the learner's increasing confidence in their own learning. The last kind is akin to self-actualization and would, most likely, work best for mature individuals. This, however, is a lengthy process, and the time needed might not be available in SEDPs. The learning method may, therefore, have to put more emphasis on other forms of reinforcement.

APPLICATION OF LEARNING

The purpose of most training of managers and administrators is to improve their decision making skills in actual work situations. Potential application of the learning in real life situations significantly enhances their motivation for learning. Further, if the process of learning is also similar to real life situations, the training method would be still more motivating.

Introductory Module

Appendix 6:
Planning and management of
short-duration, executive
development programmes

CHARACTERISTICS

Short-duration, executive development programmes (SEDPs) based particularly on application of the case method are characterized by the following:

(i)   Heterogeneity of participants with respect to age, education, maturity level, breadth of experience, exposure to organizational cultures within and across countries, motivation level, work culture in organizations they belong to, etc. These differences could be a source of strength, as they bring to bear a multifaceted view on the issues under consideration. However, they could also be the source of serious weaknesses, because they could lead to slow progress in preparation and in class discussions, particularly in the early part of the programme, as participants would take longer to understanding each other's views.

(ii)   Heterogeneity of participant's expectations both in academic and non-academic terms. These range from those who consider such programmes to be 'paid holidays' (thus looking for non-academic satisfactions like stay arrangements, food, etc.), through those who consider themselves merely 'observers' (and thus hardly participate actively) and those who are interested seriously in only some aspect of the programme (demanding far more emphasis on it), to those whose expectations match with what is being offered by the programme.

(iii)   Heterogeneity of expectations of the sponsoring organizations and executives, ranging from providing a holiday as a reward, through enabling executives to establish contacts with executives in other organizations, acquiring knowledge, gaining skills, etc., to be able to shoulder current or possible higher responsibilities, to those using the course as a building block in the career development of their executives.

(iv)   Lack of understanding about the case method and participant's responsibilities.

(v)   Limited time and flexibility available to the programme coordinator and faculty to adjust the programme plan and implementation to suit such diverse expectations, particularly at short notice.

PROBLEMS IN MANAGING SEDPs

The special characteristics of SEDPs give rise to some typical problems in planning and implementing the programmes as well as the class sessions. These pertain to some difficulties particularly faced on the first day, extended 'switch off' of some participants, domination by a few in class, mid-programme blues faced by participants, chance of total breakdown in some programmes, and non-academic concerns of the participants.

FIRST-DAY PROBLEMS

The most typical problem on the first day is that of lack of preparation, even reading, by the participants. This can arise in spite of advance mailing of material and written communication emphasizing prior preparation. The problem arises not merely because of lack of time to go through the material but more because of lack of understanding of requirements of the case method on the part of most participants.

SOME PARTICIPANTS SWITCH OFF ...

Some participants could switch off for extended periods because of:

- perceived irrelevance of topics and cases, or incomprehensibility of programme pedagogy,
- domination in discussion by only a few (including the faculty),
- difficulty in understanding language and terminologies, or
- a feeling of being out of place for some other reasons.

The resource person and other participants may also inadvertently contribute to this phenomenon. It may be helpful to build a system and learning climate in which attention gets paid to individuals so that the phenomenon is avoided and, even if it occurs, the programme coordinator and resource persons may be able to detect it promptly and take appropriate actions.

... WHILE OTHERS DOMINATE

Some participants might try to dominate the discussion in particular sessions because of their 'expertise' in the particular situation or decision area, as well as their personal need to show off. Those having significantly greater need to show off might in fact end up dominating the discussion in several sessions. Over time, this might become frustrating to other participants as well as the faculty members. Steps need to be taken by both the participants and the instructor to use the expertise available in the group without allowing domination by some to the detriment of learning by others, as well as the effects on group learning.

ALL FACE MID-PROGRAMME BLUES

Almost all programmes of one to several weeks' duration are found to exhibit what can be termed as 'mid-programme blues.' This phenomenon strikes somewhere around the time when 40 to 60% of the course is over. The primary reason seems to be the nature of the heavy workload in case-based programmes, coupled with a feeling of 'we are over the hump.' As a result, the following day's classes are a washout as the previous evening would go in merry making, general discussion, etc. The programme coordinator should consciously plan for such a contingency and/or forewarn the resource person leading the discussion on such a day.

TOTAL BREAKDOWN

Once in a while – again, somewhere around the middle of a programme – a strong feeling develops among participants that they are reaching nowhere in terms of their learning vis-à-vis the programme, the methodology, the arrangements and probably even the resource person. While this occurrence in well-managed programmes is rare, it indicates several shortcomings in design and implementation of programmes. A careful programme coordinator can salvage the programme if he or she can sense the feeling in time and if the faculty is cooperative.

NON-ACADEMIC CONCERNS

In spite of the fact that the primary purpose of any SEDP is academic, sometimes the facilities of food, accommodation, group discussion and classroom become irritants to participants. If the case is genuine and the dissatisfaction justified, the coordinator should try to take ameliorative action. However, more often than not, the dissatisfaction reflects deeper maladies related to individuals, the programme, or both. They need to be noticed early so that they can be diagnosed and appropriate remedial action taken.

SUGGESTIONS TO THE PROGRAMME COORDINATOR

The programme coordinator plays a crucial role in planning, implementing and evaluating a management development programme. In this context, the coordinator, together with programme faculty, specifies objectives, decides the target participant profile, and chooses the contents of the programme and its pedagogy. He or she also plans for and obtains feedback from participants in order to assess the programme and to suggesting improvements to the next coordinator and faculty members.

Screening participants

It is the responsibility of the programme coordinator, with help from programme faculty, to screen the participants for their suitability for the programme. Screening is done to check whether the participants have:

- the requisite capabilities to be able to benefit from the programme,
- the required motivation to learn, and
- the possibility to use the learning for their own and their organization's benefit.

Effective screening is likely to reduce the chances of uninterested participants joining the programme, and thereby avoiding or minimizing a variety of problems faced in managing the programme. In fact, the presence of properly screened candidates would go a long way in building the learning climate in the programme.

A series of steps could help in proper screening of applicants:

- proper design of the programme announcement, advertisement or brochure,
- proper design of the programme application form,

- screening by programme faculty on the basis of written communication, and

- if needed and possible, personal interview with the potential candidate and sponsoring executive.

The programme announcement or advertisement should clearly state the objectives, the profile of participants for whom the programme is meant, the content and didactic approach. The programme brochure should have details about these aspects so that the potential applicants and their sponsoring organizations can make up their mind about the suitability of candidates for the programme. The programme application form should be divided into two parts, one for the sponsoring executive and the other for the applicant executive. Specific questions about:

- expectations from the programme,

- how would the participation of the executive benefit the executive and the organization, and

- special aspects supporting the candidature of the executives may be included.

At the time of reviewing the applicant for acceptance by the faculty these details could be useful. In more uncertain cases, additional correspondence or personal discussion could be necessary to assess the participant's capabilities, motivation and likely benefits vis-à-vis the programme.

Planning the course and teaching material

Planning and scheduling of modules, sessions and teaching material in any programme should be so done as to achieve the programme objectives. At the same time, these should match with the contents and pedagogy. The case method imposes some additional requirements.

The first day

The first day, problems may arise because of not setting the stage for the programme. The coordinator should plan to devote part of the first day to clarification of the objectives of the programme, delimiting the coverage of the programme, the case method teaching approach to be used, and emphasizing the participants' role and responsibilities in the case method for getting the best learning results from the programme.

A short but comprehensive case covering most issues to be handled in the programme could be well utilized to achieve all these purposes. This exercise may be taken up over an extended session (or double session, depending on the length of the case and programme).

The programme material of the first day could be sent in advance to participants so as to provide time for reading. However, the coordinator should still expect some of the participants to arrive at the venue without the material or without preparation, or both. The extended session, as proposed above, should be used to provide time for reading (to those who did not do so) and for (further) analysis of the case by those who took time to prepare.

A separate session, whether in or out of class, should be planned for not merely introducing the participants and the faculty to each other but also to break the ice among them. Increased familiarity with each other has been found to go a long way in group and participative learning, through exchange of each other's experiences.

The programme coordinator should also plan a meeting of the programme faculty or resource persons on the day before the beginning of the programme, to take stock of the situation.

On Subsequent Days

As the time required to prepare each case is significant, usually not more than three sessions of 70-90 minutes duration should be scheduled on each of the following days. It may be ideal to have two case sessions and make the third session a lecture and discussion by internal faculty or a practising executive.

As the programme progresses, cases and reading materials for subsequent sessions could be increased in length and complexity. However, they should not become too burdensome, and yet provide enough challenge for motivating the participants to put demonstrate their best. Depending on reading speed, 50 to 100 pages (prepared in 1½ or double spacing on quarto or A4) would probably be appropriate.

For building appropriate interest among the participants, cases could describe recent situations, be well written and pertain to organizations and situations resembling those from which participants are drawn. The programme coordinator's task is catalytic. If required, she or he might initiate efforts to develop some new cases.

The last day of the programme should be planned to provide an opportunity to grapple with a situation which encompasses issues discussed in the programme. Sometimes this could be done through a very complex case. Presentations by participants on such an occasion could provide a serious assessment of participants' learning during the programme.

Designing a learning climate

The programme coordinator must take a lead in providing a proper learning climate for the programme as a whole. To counteract the switching-off phenomenon as well as lack of interest in various topics, the participants should be divided into small groups for purposes of discussion and syndicate work. The membership of such groups should be heterogeneous enough to provide representation of varied views on any specific situation. Group discussions are likely to take place in a free atmosphere, lead to clarifications on the case situation, enhance learning from each other's experiences, help weed out arguments, decisions or action plans which are *prima facie* irrelevant and, possibly, trigger some introspection about attitudes and values on the part of participants.

Besides diversity in group membership, time and space should be provided for group meetings with at least a chalkboard. If the programme is residential, participants could fix their own timing for group discussions. However, if the programme is non-residential, it may be beneficial to explicitly schedule time for preparation and group discussion.

The programme coordinator could also persuade faculty scheduled to lead classes on a particular day to be available the day before as well, for clarifications in case individual participants or groups need such help. This is seen to go a long way in generating motivation among participants.

Monitoring and reviewing the programme

As already mentioned, the programme coordinator needs to monitor the teaching and discussion in the classroom, in small groups, and even individual preparation. This could be achieved by attending class sessions, interacting with participants in their syndicate groups, and in informal discussions. Another important mechanism is daily meetings with programme faculty to review the progress of group learning, group behaviour, individual learning and individual behaviour. The coordinator should consciously look for positive and negative signals, both formal and informal, and initiate corrective steps. Interaction with participants would also help in identifying not only participants who are likely to switch off, participants who dominate discussions, or when a total breakdown situation is imminent, but also their possible causes in advance. Initiating corrective steps either on one's own initiative or with the help of programme faculty then becomes much easier.

Another aspect of monitoring and review is the task of obtaining feedback from participants on objectives, content, pedagogy, and support services. The coordinator generally plans to obtain such feedback towards the end of the programme, and both in writing through a questionnaire, and orally in a group session scheduled for feedback and review. The feedback needs to be summarized, circulated to programme faculty and passed on to the next coordinator.

SUGGESTIONS TO PROGRAMME FACULTY

The programme faculty help the coordinator in planning and implementing the programme in general. The primary task of faculty, however, is planning and implementing the module sessions assigned to them. Planning of the first and the last case session of the programme has special significance. They also, help the coordinator in planning the programme and other aspects.

First and last sessions

In a sense the two sessions are similar. The first session primarily sets the stage for the programme in terms of objectives, coverage of contents, pedagogy and role and responsibility of participants and their behaviour. The last session should focus on a complex situation, providing an opportunity to tackle it and apply the lessons taught during the programme. The faculty member conducting these sessions has additional responsibility, which is best discharged with the involvement of the coordinator and other faculty members of the programme. In fact, the presence and involvement of the entire faculty in these two sessions would demonstrate commitment and involvement of the faculty, as well as result in a more cohesive approach to learning in the programme.

Planning the programme

The programme faculty help the coordinator in screening applicants for the programme. However, their prime responsibility is for planning and conducting the module sessions assigned to them. In this respect it is advisable for the programme faculty to discuss – with the coordinator as well as other members of the programme faculty – the objectives of their sessions and modules, the materials to be used, and any interlinkages with other sessions.

The choice of cases and reading material, as suggested earlier, should be guided by the learning objectives of each sessions, the profile of participants attending the programme and the timing of the particular session in the module and the programme. This is a crucial planning decision, as this is likely to significantly influence the level of motivation and preparation during the programme.

Having chosen the material, the programme faculty should take a lead in scheduling double sessions or two sessions for long or complex cases, if needed, as well as in scheduling specific syndicate work or presentations at appropriate points. These aspects should also be discussed with the coordinator as well as the programme faculty in informal and formal meetings.

Other aspects

Helping the coordinator and other faculty members in monitoring the programme by sharing information about learning, group functioning, and any significant unexpected developments, constitute other tasks of faculty members. They could also take care of any negative developments during the course of the programme, in consultation with the programme coordinator.

SUGGESTIONS TO PARTICIPANTS

Participants play a crucial role in enriching the learning of not only individual participants but also of the entire group.

A participant thinking of attending a case-based SEDP should be prepared to spend long hours, day after day, to seriously involve him- or herself in the programme, be open and willing to share and exchange knowledge, skills and experiences with co-participants. The greater the degree to which these elements are present in individual participants, the greater the chances of better learning in a programme.

Participants would benefit greatly by being patient and trying to understanding the point of view of other participants. This helps in assimilating knowledge, skills and attitudes possessed by others. An early assimilation of these would also result in avoiding or reducing the frustration experienced by participants in the early parts of the programme regarding the nature and extent of learning, as well as the process of case discussion. The primary reason for the frustration or switch-off syndrome seems to lie in lack of understanding and appreciation of the views of other participants.

Reaching out to participants as well as faculty, whenever time permits, could help enrich one's experience and knowledge. Each participant probably has a unique fund of knowledge and experience, quite different from others. In general, the participants must put in as much as they can because, in this method, they gain in direct proportion to their input.

Participants should share their discomfort, difficulties and views about any aspect of the programme with the programme coordinator, who is likely to be in the best position to respond positively.

Participants may like to share details of some challenging situations they faced with each other and with faculty. These may not only enrich the learning of the participants but could also be potential case leads.

REFERENCES CITED AND SOURCES FOR FURTHER READING

Arnon, I. 1968. *Organization and Administration of Agricultural Research.* Amsterdam: Elsevier.

Christensen, C.R. 1987. *Teaching and the Case Method* (rev. ed.) Boston: Harvard Business School.

Copeland, M.T. 1964. *And Mark an Era: The Story of the Harvard Business School.* New York, NY: Harper and Row.

Culliton, J.W. 1973. *Handbook on Case Writing.* Makati, the Philippines: Asian Institute of Management.

Dixit, M.R., & Jain, A.K. 1985. Experiences with the case method in short duration executive development programmes. *in: Proceedings of the Third International Conference: Case Method Research and Case Method Application.* London: City University.

McNair, M.P., & Hersu, A.C. (eds) 1954. *The Case Method at the Harvard Business School.* New York, NY: McGraw-Hill.

Reynolds, J.I. 1980. *Case Method in Management Development: Guide for Effective Use.* Geneva: ILO.

Rao, S.S. 1989. The Case Method: An overview. Indian Institute of Management, Ahmedabad (mimeo.).

ILO. 1986. Teaching and Training Methods for Management Development. Geneva: ILO.